CLASSICS *for* YOUNG READERS

D1530914

TABLE OF CONTENTS

LESSONS LEARNED

FOLK TALES OF MANY LANDS

NORSE MYTHS

Tales of Hans Christian Andersen

Poetry

Voyages

AT ODDS

FOR THE FUN OF IT

LESSONS LEARNED

THE NECKLACE OF TRUTH

1

There once was a little girl named Pearl, who had the bad habit of telling lies. For a long time her father and mother did not find this out, but at last they saw that she very often said things that were not true.

Now at this time—for it was long, long ago—there was a wonderful man named Merlin. He could do such strange things, and was so wise, that he was called a wizard.

Merlin was one of the greatest friends of truth that ever lived. For this reason, children who told lies were often brought to him so that he might cure them of this bad habit.

"Let us take our child to the wonderful wizard," said Pearl's father.

And the mother said, "Yes, let us take her to Merlin. He will cure her!"

So Pearl's parents went to the palace where Merlin lived.

When they reached Merlin's palace, the mother began to tell the wise old man what was the matter with the child. "I know very well what is the matter with her, my dear madam," said Merlin. "Your child is one of the greatest liars in the world."

How did he know this? I cannot say, but this wizard could tell a liar, even though many miles away.

Poor Pearl hid her head with shame and fear. But Merlin said, "Do not be afraid. I am only going to give you a present."

Then the wizard opened a drawer and took from it a lovely necklace with a diamond clasp. This he put on Pearl's neck and told her parents to go home happy, for the little girl would soon be cured of her bad habit.

As they were going away, Merlin looked sternly at Pearl, and said, "In a year from now I shall come for my necklace. Till then you must not take it off—you must not dare take it off."

2

Now, this necklace that Merlin gave Pearl was the wonderful Necklace of Truth.

Next day, Pearl went out to play. When her neighbors saw her beautiful necklace, they crowded around her.

"Oh, what a lovely necklace! Where did you get it, Pearl?"

"My father gave it to me for a Christmas present," said Pearl. (This, you know, was a falsehood.)

"Oh, look, look!" cried the children. "The diamond has turned dim!"

Pearl looked down at her lovely necklace and saw that the lovely clasp was changed to coarse glass. Then she was very much afraid, and said, "I will tell you the truth. The wizard Merlin gave it to me."

At once the diamond was as bright as before.

The girls now began to laugh, because they knew that only children who told lies were sent to Merlin.

"You need not laugh," said Pearl. "Merlin sent a lovely coach to bring us. It was drawn by six white horses, and was lined with satin and had gold tassels; and his palace is all built of gems; and he praised me because I tell the truth." (But these were all fibs, as we know.)

She stopped, for the children were laughing all the time she was speaking. Then she looked at her necklace—and what do you think? It hung down to the floor! At each lie she had told, the necklace had stretched more and more.

"You are stretching the truth!" cried the little girls.

Then Pearl confessed that all she had told them was false. At once the necklace changed to its right size.

"But what did Merlin say when he gave you the necklace?" the girls asked.

"He said it was a present for a truthful"—but Pearl could not go on speaking. The necklace became so short that it nearly choked her.

"Oh no!" sobbed Pearl. "He said I was—I was—the greatest liar in the world."

The girls did not laugh now. They were sorry for poor Pearl when they saw her weeping.

So at last Pearl was cured. She saw how wrong and how foolish it is to tell falsehoods. "Never more will I tell a lie," said she. And she kept her word.

Before the year was ended, Merlin came for his necklace. He knew that Pearl did not need it now, and he wanted it for a little boy.

So many years have passed since then that no one can tell where the wonderful Necklace of Truth might be. If it should ever be found, would you like to wear it? Would you keep the diamond always bright?

The Stone in the Road

Early one morning a sturdy old farmer came along the highway with his oxcart loaded with corn. "Oh, these lazy people!" he cried, driving his oxen to one side of the road. "Here is this big stone right in the middle of the road, and nobody will take the trouble to move it!" So he went on his way, scolding about the laziness of other people.

Then along came a soldier with a bright feather in his hat and a big sword at his side. He held his head high in the air and sang a merry song. Of course he did not see the stone in the road, but stumbled over it and fell flat in the dust.

When he had picked himself up, he began to scold about the country people.

"The stupid things!" he said. "Don't they know any better than to leave a stone in the road?"

An hour later six merchants came down the road with their goods on pack horses, on their way to the fair. When they came to the stone, they carefully drove their horses around it.

"Did anyone ever see such a thing?" they said. "There is that big stone in the road and not one man in all the country will pick it up!"

The stone lay there for three weeks. It was in everybody's way. Wouldn't you think that someone might have taken the trouble to move it? But no! Each man grumbled about it and left it for somebody else to move.

Then one day the king sent word to all his people to meet on the highway, for he had something to tell them.

Soon a great crowd of men and women gathered in the road. The farmer was there, and so were the merchants and the young soldier.

"I hope the king will now find out what lazy people he has around him," said the soldier.

"I shall not be surprised," said the farmer, "if the king has something to say about how these people leave stones in the road."

At length the sound of a horn was heard, and the king came riding toward them. When he reached the stone he said, "My friends, I put this stone in the road three weeks ago. Each and every one of you has seen it. Each man has scolded his neighbor, but not one of you has taken the trouble to move the stone."

Then the king got down from his horse and rolled the stone over. Underneath it in a round hollow place, lay a small iron box. He held up the box so that the people might see the piece of paper fastened to it. On the paper were written these words:

For him who lifts the stone.

The king opened the box and turned it upside down. Out fell a beautiful gold ring and twenty bright coins.

"These," said he, "were waiting for the man who would move the stone instead of finding fault with his neighbors."

BRUCE AND THE SPIDER

Long ago, Robert Bruce, the king of Scotland, was hiding one day in a little hut that lay deep in the forest. He was all alone and much discouraged. He had been fighting many battles with the enemies of Scotland and had lost every battle. His soldiers had been killed or driven to take refuge in the mountains, as the king himself was now doing. He was hungry and homeless. He had no food and no place of shelter but a mean hut.

"There is no use in trying to free Scotland now," thought the king. "Our enemies are too strong. I might as well give up the struggle."

Just then he saw a spider trying to spin a web between two rafters. She would fasten one end of her thread to a rafter, and then swing herself across to the other rafter. She seemed to find this very hard, for each time the thread broke, and the spider would have to begin all over again.

Bruce sat watching her, and wondered how long she would keep trying before she gave up. Six times the spider tried to fasten her thread, and six times she failed.

"You are a brave and patient spider," thought the king. "You do not give up as soon as I do. I will watch you try the seventh time. If you succeed, I too will risk my seventh battle."

Once more the spider swung her tiny thread to the opposite rafter, and this time it held fast.

"You have taught me a lesson, little spider," said Bruce. "I will gather my army and try once more to drive away the enemies of Scotland."

So the king stood again at the head of his army, and he fought as he had never fought before. This time, he won the battle and made his country free.

Columbus at the Court of Spain

Scene 1

Characters:

ISABELLA, QUEEN OF SPAIN
DON GOMEZ, ADVISOR TO THE KING AND QUEEN
CHRISTOPHER COLUMBUS, A SEA CAPTAIN
FROM ITALY

Time:

APRIL, 1492

Place:

A ROOM IN THE PALACE

Columbus has been telling the queen of his belief that that he can reach India by sailing west. He has asked for help so he can make the voyage to prove he is right.

ISABELLA: Don Gomez, you have heard what this captain has said. Do you think we ought to help him?

DON GOMEZ: Your majesty, his plan is all a wild dream. I am a plain, matter-of-fact man and do not see such visions.

ISABELLA: But Columbus has given us good reasons for his beliefs and plans.

DON GOMEZ: But, your majesty, I am a plain, matter-of-fact man, and I say we must look at the facts. Surely we know that the unknown seas to the west are filled with monsters that can swallow a ship in a single mouthful.

COLUMBUS: Men have sailed far out of sight upon the ocean and have come back safely. I, too, shall be able to bring my ships home.

DON GOMEZ: Your majesty, I am a plain, matter-of-fact man. The fact is, even if the sea monsters do not swallow Columbus's ships, we know that far off, where the sun sinks into the ocean, the boiling waters will burn a ship like a dry leaf in a flame.

COLUMBUS: Your majesty, there are many things about the earth that men have not yet learned. But I have studied long, and I have faith that I will find the lands I seek.

DON GOMEZ *(Sneering):* Oh, very well. Very well! But I say we must believe the facts.

ISABELLA: Then you think we should listen no longer to the words of Columbus?

DON GOMEZ: It is all folly! I am sure of it. Columbus speaks of faith, but I insist on facts.

ISABELLA: Don Gomez, have you ever seen anyone from the unknown land to which we go after death?

DON GOMEZ *(Surprised):* Certainly not. But I have faith that we shall go there.

ISABELLA: Columbus, too, has faith. It is by faith that he looks across the vast ocean to the distant land.

COLUMBUS: Your majesty is right. But I also have strong reasons for the faith that is in me. I know that I can sail far to the west and find the new way to India.

DON GOMEZ: Oh, yes, sail away—and we shall never hear of you again. You must give us facts, solid facts, before we plain, matter-of-fact people will risk money on your plans. Your majesty, pay no more heed to him. Why, even the boys on the street laugh when he passes.

ISABELLA: Do you think I care for the jeering of boys who laugh at what they do not understand? I have faith in all that this earnest man has said. I am ready to test his great and glorious plan, even though you call it folly. The fact is, Don Gomez, we do not know what lies to the west, for none among us has yet dared to brave those trackless waters.

DON GOMEZ: Your majesty will pardon me if I remind you of what the king himself has said. He has no money to help Columbus.

ISABELLA: But I have jewels of great value, which I will use to raise the money that Columbus needs. It shall be done without delay.

COLUMBUS: Your majesty shall never regret this noble decision. I shall return and lay at your feet such a jewel as has never been worn by any queen. I know that I shall succeed and that the world shall forever remember you for your decision today.

SCENE 2

Characters:

DON GOMEZ
HIS SECRETARY

Time:

MARCH, 1493

Place:

THE OFFICE OF DON GOMEZ

DON GOMEZ: What! What is this you tell me? Columbus has returned? He crossed the western ocean and has come back safe and sound? He escaped the sea monsters? He wasn't boiled alive? Impossible!

SECRETARY: It is so, Don Gomez. A messenger arrived at the palace an hour ago. Columbus has landed. The news is spreading. All Spain will be wild with excitement.

DON GOMEZ: A trick! It must be a trick!

SECRETARY: But Columbus has brought home proof of his voyage. He has brought gold, precious stones, and strange plants and animals.

DON GOMEZ: Still, I say it is a trick. I say he has been sailing along the coast of Africa and has picked up a few things. Now he pretends these are proofs of his discovery. A plain, matter-of-fact man, such as I am, is not taken in by such a ridiculous story.

SECRETARY: The queen has given orders to receive him at court with the greatest honors.

DON GOMEZ: What a mistake! Her majesty is too quick to believe whatever she is told. Mark my words, it will all turn out to be a trick. We shall find that Columbus sailed south instead of west and didn't discover anything.

SECRETARY: But the sailors all say they steered west.

DON GOMEZ: A trick! A trick! Would you have me believe he has reached an unknown coast by sailing west through the unknown seas? Impossible! I am a plain, matter-of-fact man, sir. I know the facts. Call my carriage. I must go to the palace and show the queen that Columbus is all wrong. Come! Let us go!

[Exit.]

DANIEL WEBSTER'S FIRST CASE

Perhaps you have heard the name of Daniel Webster, one of the greatest lawyers who ever lived in our country. Someday you may read his speeches, and then you will learn how well he could speak before a judge when a man was tried for his life, or when any other great case was in court.

Here is a story about Daniel Webster's first case. It was his very first, for Daniel was at this time only ten years old.

Daniel's father was a poor farmer. Besides Daniel, he had an older son, Ezekiel. Both boys used to help him do farm work.

One day Ezekiel set a trap to catch a woodchuck, which for a long time had been stealing his breakfast from the garden of the Websters. At last the woodchuck was caught.

"Now," cried Ezekiel, "we'll kill the thief. You've done harm enough, Mr. Woodchuck, and now you shall die!"

Daniel, who had a kind heart, begged his brother not to kill the poor thing, but to take him into the woods and let him go. Ezekiel refused to do this. And so, as they could not agree, the two lads went to their father and asked him what should be done.

"Well," said old Mr. Webster, "here is the prisoner. Let us try him for his life. Ezekiel, you shall be the lawyer against him. Daniel, you shall be the lawyer for him. You may both speak. I will be the judge."

Ezekiel began. He spoke about the harm the woodchuck had done in the garden. He told how much time and trouble it took to catch him. He asked if the prisoner would not surely take to his bad habit again if they should let him go. And he ended with these words: "The prisoner must die. And, to pay for the harm he has done, let us sell his skin!"

Ezekiel spoke well, and old Mr. Webster seemed to think he was right. Now he turned to his younger son and said, "I'll hear now what you have to say, Daniel."

Daniel was very much afraid that his brother had won the case. But, seeing the poor woodchuck trembling in his prison, the boy's breast swelled with pity. Looking the judge full in the face with his deep black eyes, Daniel began.

"Ezekiel has spoken well, but he forgets some things. I say the woodchuck has a right to life, to food, and to freedom. God made him to live in the bright sunshine, in the free fields and woods.

"He is not like the cruel fox, for he kills nothing. He only eats a little of our corn, and I am sure we have

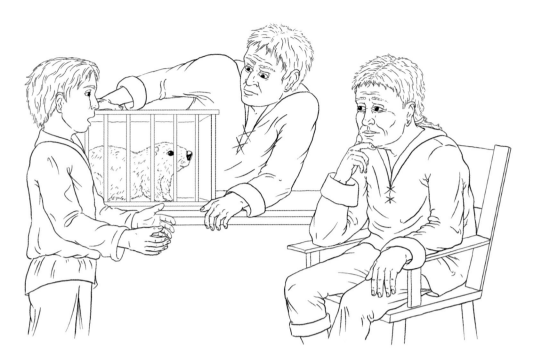

plenty. Has he taken anything but the little food he needed to keep him alive? And is not that food as sweet to him as the food on Mother's table is to us?

"You can't say he has broken laws, as men often do. He has only done what it is his nature to do. How, then, can you blame him? Look at the poor, trembling creature, and answer me this: How dare you take away that life that you can never give back again?"

Daniel paused. There were tears in his father's eyes—tears that rolled down his sunburnt cheeks. The plea for mercy had touched the old man's heart. Forgetting that he was the "judge," he started up, and cried in a loud voice, "Zeke, Zeke, you let that woodchuck go!"

If ever you are tempted to tease or hurt a poor creature, remember Daniel Webster's first case. Think of his words of mercy, and "let the woodchuck go."

FOLK TALES OF MANY LANDS

THE LEAK IN THE DIKE

In Western Europe, there is a country called The Netherlands, which people also call Holland. Holland borders on the North Sea. There is something very unusual about the land of Holland. A large part of the land is lower than the level of the sea. The people have built great walls, called dikes, to keep the water from flooding their cities and homes. These dikes are high and wide, and sometimes covered with buildings and trees. Here is an old story from Holland.

Many years ago there lived in Holland a brave, happy little boy named Peter.

Peter's father was a man who watched the gates in the dikes, and opened and closed them for the ships to pass out of the canals into the great sea.

Even the little children were taught that the dikes must be watched every moment, and that a hole no larger than your little finger was a very dangerous thing.

One lovely afternoon in the early fall, when Peter was eight years old, his mother called him from his play. "Come, Peter," she said, "I wish you to go across the dike and take these cakes to your friend, the blind man. If you go quickly, and do not stop to play, you will be home again before it is dark."

The little boy was glad to go on such an errand, and started off with a light heart. He stayed with the blind man a little while to tell him about his walk along the dike—of the sun and the flowers and the ships far out at sea. Then he remembered his mother's wish that he should return before dark. He bid his friend goodbye and set out for home.

As he walked beside the canal, he noticed how the rains had swollen the waters, and how they beat against the side of the dike, and he thought of his father's gates.

"I am glad they are so strong," he said to himself. "If they gave way what would become of us? These fields would be covered with water. Father always calls them the 'angry waters.' I suppose he thinks they are angry at him for keeping them out so long."

As he walked along he sometimes stopped to pick the pretty blue flowers that grew beside the road, or to listen to the rabbits' soft tread as they rustled through the grass. He smiled as he thought of his visit to the blind man, who was always so glad to be visited.

Suddenly he noticed that the sun was setting and that it was growing dark. "Mother will be watching for me," he thought, and he began to run toward home.

Just then he heard a noise. It was a dripping, trickling sound. He stopped and looked down. There was a small hole in the dike, through which a tiny stream was flowing.

Any child in Holland is frightened at the thought of a leak in the dike. Peter understood the danger at once. If the water ran through a little hole, it would soon make a larger one, and the whole country would be flooded. In a moment he saw what he must do. Throwing away his flowers, he climbed down the side of the dike and thrust his finger into the tiny hole.

The flowing of the water was stopped!

"Oho!" he said to himself. "The angry waters must stay back now. I can keep them back with my finger. Holland shall not be drowned while I am here."

This was all very well at first, but it soon grew dark and cold. The little fellow shouted, "Hello! Is anyone there? Come here!" But no one heard him; no one came to help him.

It grew still colder. His arm ached and began to grow stiff and numb. He shouted again, "Will no one come? Mother! Mother!"

Many times since sunset, his mother had looked anxiously along the dike road for her little boy. Now she had closed and locked the cottage door, thinking that Peter was spending the night with his blind friend, and that she would scold him in the morning for staying away from home without her permission.

Peter tried to whistle, but his teeth chattered with cold. He thought of his brother and sister in their warm beds, and of his dear father and mother. "I must not let them be drowned," he thought. "I must stay here until someone comes, if I have to stay all night."

The moon and stars looked down on the child crouching on a stone on the side of the dike. His head was bent, and his eyes were closed, but he was not asleep, for every now and then he rubbed the hand that was holding back the angry sea.

In the early morning, a laborer going to his work thought he heard a groan as he walked along on the top of the dike. Bending down he saw the child, and called to him: "What is the matter, boy? Are you hurt? Why are you sitting there?"

"I am keeping the water from running in," was the answer of the little hero. "Tell them to come quickly."

WILLIAM TELL

1

Many, many years ago, a cruel tyrant named Gessler ruled over Switzerland. He was a stern, hard ruler. He hated the Swiss people, and most of all he hated a man named William Tell.

Tell was a strong, brave man. No one else could shoot an arrow as straight as he could. No one else could sail a boat as skillfully over a stormy lake. Gessler hated William Tell because he was brave and true, and because he loved freedom and right.

One day Tell and his young son Albert fell into the power of Gessler's soldiers. The tyrant was glad to hear of this. He tried to think of the cruelest way to punish Tell.

"Let the man shoot at an apple a hundred paces away," he said. "If he can hit it, I will spare his life." Then with a sneer he added, "And the apple must rest on his son's head."

Tell refused to try to save his life in such a way. He was very skillful, but he could not be sure of hitting an apple so far away without harming the boy.

Albert was a brave boy. He begged his father to try. "You will not hit me, Father," he said. "I know you will hit the apple and then we shall both be free."

Tell again refused to try. At last Gessler cried angrily, "Come, make the trial. If you do not, your boy shall die at once. I give you one chance to save his life. Use it."

There was nothing else that Tell could do.

The soldiers marked off a hundred paces. They led Albert forward and placed the apple on his head. The boy stood there, straight and fearless.

Tell chose two arrows. He placed one in his belt and the other on his bow. Then he took aim carefully.

The arrow hissed through the air and flew straight to the core of the apple. The boy was unharmed.

"Father!" he cried, "I'm safe!" He ran to his father and clasped him about the neck.

2

Before Tell could move, Gessler asked, "Why did you place that second arrow in your belt?"

"To kill you, if I had slain my boy," answered Tell.

Gessler was very angry. "I have promised you your life," he said, "but you shall spend it in darkness, in a prison where neither sun nor moon can shine upon you."

Turning to his soldiers, he added, "Let the boy go, but take the man to my boat."

Instantly the soldiers seized William Tell and bound him. They carried him to the small boat in which Gessler was to return to his castle.

Soon after they set sail, a great storm sprang up. The winds and waves tossed the boat from side to side. Gessler's men were frightened, for not one of them could manage the boat in such a furious storm.

Gessler feared that they would all be drowned. He knew that William Tell could steer the boat safely, so at last he gave orders that the prisoner should be unbound.

Tell headed the boat straight for the land. As it touched the shore, he gave a great leap to the rocks and dashed away.

The boat slipped back into deep water so that the others could not follow him. While they were tossing about on the lake, Tell escaped, and before the storm was over, he was out of reach of the tyrant.

Dick Whittington and His Cat

1

Many years ago in England there lived a boy named Richard Whittington, but everyone called him Dick. Dick's father and mother died when he was a baby, and the woman who took care of him was very poor. Sometimes he had no breakfast or dinner, and he was often glad to get a crust of dry bread.

In spite of this, Dick grew to be a very bright boy. He liked to listen when people were talking, and in this way he learned a great deal.

He often heard the village people speak of London. They had never seen this great city. But they believed that all the streets were paved with gold and silver, that everyone there was very rich, and that singing and music could be heard all the day long.

One day a wagon entered the little town where Dick lived. It was drawn by eight black horses with bells on their heads. Dick saw the wagon standing before the door of the inn. He thought that anything so fine must surely be going to London.

When the driver came out, Dick asked him if he might walk by the side of the wagon. When the driver learned that the lad had no father or mother, and that he was very poor, the man told him he might go with him if he wished.

It was a long walk for the little fellow, but at last he came to the great city of London. He was in such a hurry to see the streets paved with gold and silver that he ran about all day trying to find one.

He had once seen a piece of gold money. He knew that it would buy a great many things. So he thought that if he could pick up a bit of gold pavement, he could buy everything he wanted.

Poor Dick ran about till he was tired. It began to grow dark, and he had not found a single bit of gold. He sat down in a dark corner and cried himself to sleep.

In the morning he woke up very hungry, but there was not even a crust of bread for him to eat. He was so hungry that he forgot all about the gold pavement and thought only of food.

He walked up and down the streets asking everyone whom he met to give him a penny so he could buy something to eat.

"Go to work and earn one, you lazy boy," said some of them. Others passed by without looking at him.

"I wish I could go to work," thought Dick.

When he was so hungry and tired that he could go no farther, he sat down at the door of a large house. The cook, who was busy getting dinner, saw him and called out, "What are you doing there, boy? If you don't run away, I will throw this dishwater over you. I have some here that is hot enough to make you jump."

Just then the master of the house came home to dinner. When he saw the ragged boy at the door, he said, "What are you doing here, my lad? You seem to be old enough to work. I am afraid that you are a lazy little fellow."

"No, indeed, sir," said Dick. "I would be very glad to work, but I do not know anybody, and I am sick for want of food."

"Poor boy!" said Mr. Fitzwarren. "Come in, and I will see if I can help you."

The kind merchant gave the lad a good dinner, and then told the cook to give him some work.

Dick would have been very happy in this new home if it had not been for the cross cook. She scolded him from morning till night, and often boxed his ears and hit him with the broom.

At last, little Alice, Mr. Fitzwarren's daughter, heard how he was treated. She told the cook that she would be sent away if she were not kinder to the lad.

After that, he was better treated, but he had another trouble. His bed was in the garret, and at night great numbers of rats and mice came through the holes in the floor and made so much noise that he was not able to sleep.

2

One day a gentleman gave Dick a penny for cleaning his shoes. Dick thought he would buy a cat with it. The next morning he saw a girl who was carrying a cat in her arms.

"I will give you this penny for your cat," he said.

"Very well, you may have her," said the girl. "You will find that she is an excellent mouser."

Dick kept his cat in the garret and gave her a part of his dinner each day. In a short time, there was not a rat or a mouse to trouble him, and he slept soundly every night.

Soon after this, Mr. Fitzwarren had a ship ready to sail on a trading voyage. He called his servants together and asked them if they had anything to send in the ship for trade.

Everyone had something to send but Dick. As he had neither money nor goods, he stayed in the kitchen.

Little Alice missed him and guessed why he did not come. She said to her father, "Poor Dick ought to have a chance, too, Papa. I have a little money in my purse. May I not send it for him?"

"No, my child," said the merchant. "Each one must send something of his own." Then he said to one of the men, "Tell Dick to come here."

When the lad came into the room, Mr. Fitzwarren said to him, "What are you going to send out on my ship?"

"I have nothing, sir," replied the boy, "nothing but my cat, which I bought for a penny."

"Bring your cat, then, my good boy," said the merchant. "Let her go on the voyage. Perhaps some good may come of it."

Dick went up to the garret and brought down poor puss. With tears in his eyes, he took her to the captain of the vessel.

Everybody laughed at Dick's odd venture. But Alice felt sorry for the little boy and gave him money to buy another cat. This act of kindness made the cook jealous of poor Dick. She made fun of him for sending his cat to sea, and she made him work harder than ever.

At last Dick could bear her no longer. He made up his mind to run away. He started early in the morning and walked far out into the country. There he sat on a stone, which to this day is called "Whittington's Stone."

While he was wondering what he should do next, the bells of Bow Church began to ring. He listened, and they seemed to say to him:

Turn again, Whittington,
Lord Mayor of London.

"Lord Mayor of London," he said to himself. "I would do almost anything to be Lord Mayor of London and ride in a fine coach when I am a man! I will go back and think nothing of the fussing and scolding of the old cook, if I may be Lord Mayor at last."

So Dick went back. He was lucky enough to get into the kitchen and set about his work before the cook came downstairs.

3

The ship, with the cat on board, had a long and stormy voyage. It was at last driven to a strange land.

The people of this country had never seen any Englishmen. They came in great crowds to see the sailors and to buy the fine things with which the ship was loaded.

The captain sent some of the most beautiful things he had to the king of the country. The king was so pleased that he sent for the captain to come to his palace.

When the captain arrived, the king and queen invited him to dine with them. A number of jeweled dishes were placed on beautiful rugs with woven patterns of gold and silver flowers. The king and queen seated themselves on soft cushions, and the captain did the same.

They had hardly begun to eat, however, when a vast number of rats and mice rushed in and helped themselves. The captain was much surprised. He asked if they did not find the rats very troublesome.

"Oh, yes," answered the king. "I would give half of my possessions to be freed from them. They not only destroy my dinner, but they disturb me in my sleep."

The captain jumped for joy, for he remembered little Whittington and his cat. He told the king that he had a creature on board the ship that would kill all these rats and mice.

Now it was the king's turn to be delighted. "Bring this creature to me," he cried. "If this creature will do what you say, I will load your ship with gold and jewels in exchange for it."

The captain pretended that he did not wish to part with the cat. He told the king that when she was gone, the rats and mice might destroy the goods in the ship. But finally he agreed to bring the cat to the palace.

"Run, run!" said the queen. "I am in a hurry to see this wonderful creature."

The captain hurried to his vessel. While he was gone, another dinner was prepared. When he returned, the table was covered with rats.

As soon as the cat saw them, she jumped from the captain's arms, and in a few minutes killed many of the rats and mice. The rest fled to their holes in terror.

The king and queen were delighted. They asked to see the creature that had driven the rats and mice away.

The captain called, "Come, kitty, kitty," and she came running to him. He handed her to the queen. She was at first afraid to touch the animal. The captain showed her how to stroke the cat gently under the chin, and soon the cat purred herself to sleep on the queen's lap.

The king wished to buy the cat at once. First he bought the whole of the ship's cargo, and then he gave the captain ten times more for the cat. The captain took leave of the king and queen, and set sail the next day for England.

4

One morning Mr. Fitzwarren had just seated himself at his desk when somebody knocked at the door. "Who's there?" asked the merchant.

"A friend," was the reply. "I come to bring you good news of your ship, the *Unicorn*."

The merchant opened the door. There stood the captain with a trunk full of gold and jewels.

He soon told Mr. Fitzwarren the story of the cat, and showed him the rich present that the king and queen had sent to Dick. As soon as the merchant heard this, he called to his servants, "Go and bring him. We will tell him of his fame. And call him Mr. Whittington by name."

Some of the servants said that so great a treasure was too much for Dick. But Mr. Fitzwarren, who was a good and honest man, answered, "I would not deprive him of a single penny."

Dick now arrived. He was very dirty, for he had been scouring kettles for the cook. The merchant ordered a chair set for him. Dick began to think they were making fun of him.

"Do not play tricks with a poor boy like me," he said. "Please let me go back to my work."

"We are not joking, Mr. Whittington," said the merchant. "The captain has sold your cat to the king of a foreign land. He has brought you in return more riches than I possess in the world."

Mr. Fitzwarren then told the man to open the box of jewels and display the treasure. Poor Dick was so amazed that he did not know what to say. He begged his master to take a part of his wealth, since he owed it all to his kindness.

"No, no," said the merchant. "It is all yours. I have no doubt that you will use it well."

Dick next asked his mistress, and then little Alice, to accept part of his treasure, but they would not do so.

The lad was too kind-hearted, however, to keep it all for himself. He gave a present to the captain and sailors, and to each of Mr. Fitzwarren's servants, not even forgetting the cross cook.

After this, the merchant advised him to dress himself like a gentleman, and invited him to live in his house till he could provide one for himself.

Years later, when Richard Whittington had grown to be a man, and was very rich and generous, he was indeed made Lord Mayor of London.

THE STONE-CUTTER

1

When Taro was a little boy, he said, "If I ever grow up to be a stone-cutter and can go up with the men in the morning and cut the great rocks from the mountainside, I shall be happy."

Years went by and Taro grew big and strong. One morning he took his hammer and set out with the men to climb the mountain and cut the rock from the mountainside.

It was a happy day for Taro. All day he swung his heavy hammer and laughed to see the great rock break and the chips fly about him. All day he worked in the hot sun, and he sang as he worked.

At nighttime, he came down the mountain, tired and happy. He was glad to eat his simple supper and go to bed. And so for many days he worked and sang.

But as time went on, he was not so happy. He grew tired of rising before the sun and climbing the mountain through the cold morning mist.

As he toiled, the hot sun beat down upon his back. The hammer blistered his hands. The sharp chips cut his face. He no longer sang at his work. Taro was tired of being a stone-cutter.

One day when he had a holiday, Taro went into town. At noon he stopped to rest before a large house that stood in the midst of beautiful rose gardens.

The door of the house opened and a man came out. He was dressed in fine silks, as soft as spiders' webs and colored like the rainbow. Jewels sparkled on his hands. Taro watched him pick the roses and drop them into a great basket carried by a servant at his side.

"Ah, me," said Taro to himself. "This must be a very rich man."

As he walked along the stony road that night, he looked at his blistered hands and thought of the rich man's jeweled fingers. When he came to his little hut at the foot of the mountain, he thought of the rich man's house in the midst of rose gardens.

He looked up at the mountain, where far above him the spirit of the mountain dwelt among the clouds and mists. He thought of how he must rise the next morning before the sun and climb up there to work all day in the burning heat.

"Oh, spirit of the mountain," cried Taro, "make me a rich man, too, so that I may wear silks as fine as spiders' webs, and live in a beautiful house, and walk in rose gardens. Then shall I be happy."

The spirit of the mountain heard and smiled. That very night the little hut vanished. In its place stood a large house in the midst of rose gardens.

2

Taro was now a very rich man. He no longer had to rise before the sun and climb the steep mountainside. He no longer had to bend all day over his work while the hot sun beat down upon his head. He could walk all day in his rose garden if he wished. But he soon became very tired of it.

One day as he stood looking out over his garden wall, a golden chariot came dashing by. It was drawn by six white horses with golden harnesses glittering in the sun. A coachman dressed in white and gold sat up on the seat in front and cracked a golden whip.

In the chariot sat a prince, dressed in purple and cloth of gold. Over his head there was a golden umbrella to shade him from the sun, and a servant ran beside him to fan him with a golden fan.

"So, this is the prince," said Taro to himself. "He is far greater than I. He rules the land for miles about. He rides in a golden chariot with a golden umbrella over his head, and a servant fans him with a golden fan."

Then Taro cried to the spirit of the mountain, "Oh, spirit, I am tired of being a rich man and walking in my rose gardens. Make me a prince who rules the land. Let

me ride in a golden chariot, with a golden umbrella over my head, and a servant to fan me with a golden fan. Then I shall surely be happy."

Again the spirit of the mountain heard and smiled, and again Taro had his wish.

In the blink of an eye, he became a prince. He lived in a fine palace. He had servants dressed in white and gold and he rode in a golden chariot with a golden umbrella over his head. He ruled the country round about, and rich and poor obeyed him.

"There is no one so great as I am," he cried. "Now I am truly happy."

3

One hot summer day Taro rode through his lands in his golden chariot. The flowers drooped by the wayside. The fields were dry and brown. He looked up at the hot sun that poured its rays upon the dry ground.

"The sun is greater than I am," cried Taro in sorrow. "Oh, spirit of the mountain, what pleasure is it to be a prince and rule the land and ride in a golden chariot with a golden umbrella over my head? The sun will not obey me. I wish I were the sun. Then I should indeed be happy."

In an instant, he was the sun. He laughed as he sent his rays down upon the backs of the poor stone-cutters on the mountain. He laughed as he saw the roses wither in the rich men's gardens, and princes try in vain to keep cool under their golden umbrellas.

"Ah, ha," he cried, as the earth turned brown and withered beneath his rays. "Now, I am really happy. I am the strongest thing in the whole wide world."

But his happiness did not last. One day a heavy cloud came between him and the earth. "Begone," cried the sun, and shone his fiercest. But the cloud still floated before him.

"Begone!" cried Taro. "Do you not see that I am the sun, the greatest thing in the world?" But still the cloud did not move.

"Alas!" cried Taro, "this cloud is greater than I. Let me be a cloud, spirit of the mountain, that I may be happy."

Once more the spirit of the mountain granted Taro's wish. He became a cloud. He hid the earth from the great sun and laughed at its rage. He sent cool showers upon the earth. The roses bloomed again. The fields grew green.

He laughed in joy at his power. He rained and rained till the rivers overflowed and the land was flooded.

Yet far up on the mountainside, the rocks stood firm. Try as he might, Taro could not move them. He poured torrents of rain upon them, but they did not stir. Because of this, Taro was not happy.

"The rocks of the mountainside are mightier than I," he cried at last. "Oh, spirit of the mountain, let me be a rock, or I shall never be really happy."

The spirit of the mountain sighed a little. But it said, "Have thy wish. Be a rock."

4

It was pleasant to be a rock. The hot sun poured down its rays and the clouds dropped their rain, but the great rock stood firm. Even the prince in his golden chariot and the rich man in his rose garden could not have moved it. Surely, now Taro was happy. But his happiness did not last.

One day a man came to the mountain. *Tap, tap, tap.* The rock shivered as the hammer struck it. *Tap, tap, tap.* The rock split from side to side, and a great piece broke off and fell to the ground.

"Oh, spirit of the mountain," cried Taro in sorrow, "man is mightier than I. Change me once more to a man and I shall be happy and contented."

Then the spirit of the mountain smiled. "Be thou a man," it said.

So Taro became a man again. He became once more the poor stone-cutter who lived at the foot of the mountain.

Every morning he rose before the sun and climbed the mountain through banks of mist. All day he bent over his work while the hot sun beat upon his head. In the evening, very tired, he climbed down the side and was glad to eat his simple supper and go to bed.

Yet Taro was happy. He had wished for many things and had tried them all. But in the end, he knew that the life of a stone-cutter suited him best.

Once more he laughed to see the great rock break and the chips fly. And once more he sang at his work.

ALADDIN AND THE WONDERFUL LAMP

1

Many years ago in Persia, there lived a poor widow and her son, Aladdin, a boy who liked to do nothing but play all day long. One day as Aladdin was playing in the streets, a man stopped and spoke to him.

"Are you not the son of Mustapha, the tailor?" asked the stranger.

"I am, sir," replied Aladdin, "but he died long ago."

Then the stranger, who was a powerful magician, embraced Aladdin and cried, "My dear boy, I am your uncle. I knew you from your likeness to my brother. Run quickly and tell your mother that I am coming."

Aladdin ran home as fast as he could to tell the news. His mother was amazed. "Indeed, child," she said, "your father had a brother, but I thought he had been dead for years."

While she prepared supper, Aladdin went to get his uncle, who came laden with food. As soon as he had greeted Aladdin's mother, the man bowed to the place where Mustapha used to sit.

"Do not be surprised that I have not come before," he said. "I have traveled far and wide and have been out of the country for many years."

When he heard that Aladdin had not yet learned a trade, he said that he would buy a shop for the boy and stock it with goods. "You shall become a rich merchant," he said.

The next day he bought Aladdin a new suit of clothes and took him all over the city, where there were many wonderful things to see. At nightfall they came home, and Aladdin's mother was overjoyed to see her son looking so fine. The stranger was so good to them that she was now sure he must indeed be the brother of Mustapha.

"I do not know how to thank you enough for all your kindness," she said. "May you live many happy years."

2

Early the next morning the man said to Aladdin, "Come, my boy. I will show you some fine things today."

He led Aladdin to a beautiful garden outside the city gates. After they had eaten and rested there, they traveled onward until they were a long, long way from the city.

Aladdin became so tired that he begged to go back, but the man told him pleasant stories and led him on and on. At last they came to a narrow valley between two mountains.

"We will go no farther," said the man. "I am now going to show you a sight such as no man ever saw. If you wish to see this sight, you must do as you are told. First, gather some dry sticks."

Aladdin quickly brought the sticks and the magician started a fire. Then he threw a powder on the flames and mumbled strange words that Aladdin could not understand.

At once, thick clouds of smoke arose, the earth beneath their feet trembled, and they heard a rumbling sound like thunder. Then the ground opened in front of them. There lay a large, flat stone with a brass ring in the center.

Aladdin started to run away in great fright, but the magician caught him and gave him a blow that knocked him down.

"What have I done, Uncle?" cried Aladdin.

Then the man spoke kindly, saying, "Fear nothing, but obey me. Beneath this stone lies a treasure, which is to be yours. No one else may touch it. If you wish to get it, you must be brave and do just as I tell you. Grasp that brass ring with your right hand. Speak the names of your father and grandfather, and pull."

Aladdin did as he was told. The stone came up as if by magic. Beneath it were steps leading into the ground.

"Now," said the magician, "go down these steps, and you will come to three long halls. Pass through them without stopping. Be careful not to touch anything, for if you do, you will surely die. Then go straight till you come to a garden of fruit trees. You may pick some of this fruit if you wish. Then walk on till you find a lighted lamp. Pour out the oil and bring the lamp to me."

He drew a ring from his finger and gave it to Aladdin, saying, "Go down boldly, child, and do as I tell you. We shall then be rich all the rest of our lives."

3

Aladdin sprang quickly down the steps. He found everything just as the magician had said. He passed through the halls and the garden of beautiful trees. Without stopping and without touching anything, he went on till he found the lighted lamp. When he had poured out the oil and placed the lamp inside his coat, he began to look about him.

Upon the trees were fruits of every color. Some were as clear as crystal, and others were red, green, blue, or purple. All sparkled in the light, for they were really precious gems. Aladdin filled his pockets and then returned to the mouth of the cave.

The magician was kneeling at the top of the steps when Aladdin began to climb them. "Hurry!" he cried. "Give me the lamp!" He reached out to take the lamp, and at the same instant he threw some powder into the fire and muttered the strange words once more.

Aladdin stopped for a moment, for he could not get the lamp from the folds of his coat. "You'll have to wait until I'm out of the cave," he said. "I can't give it to you just now."

"You must!" cried the magician. "Hand the lamp to me at once!"

"I will when I'm out of the cave," replied Aladdin. But at that instant the stone slipped back into its place. The earth closed over it, and Aladdin was left in darkness.

The magician screamed in rage. He had spoken the magic words too soon.

Now, you must know that this magician was not Aladdin's uncle. He was a cruel man who had read in his books about a wonderful lamp that would make him the most powerful man in the world. He knew where to find the lamp, but the book said that it must be placed in his hands by someone else. So he had pretended to be Aladdin's uncle in order to get the boy to help him. He had planned to get the lamp and shut Aladdin in the cave. But he spoke the magic words too soon, and so put an end to his hopes.

But poor Aladdin! He was left alone in the dark cave under the ground. He was frightened nearly to death. For two long days and nights, he sat in the cave, weeping bitterly. By the third day, he was nearly starved. He clasped his hands in prayer, and as he did so, he rubbed the ring that the magician had given him.

In an instant a huge and frightful genie appeared before him.

"What is thy will, master?" asked the genie. "I am the Genie of the Ring, and will obey thee in all things."

At any other time Aladdin might have been too frightened to speak, but now he replied boldly, "Whoever you are, if you are able, take me out of this place!"

No sooner had he spoken than the earth opened and he was once more above ground. He set off rapidly towards home, very grateful for his escape.

4

When he reached home, Aladdin emptied his pockets onto the table.

"Where did you get such strange fruit, and such a curious old lamp?" asked his mother.

"I will tell you all about it," said her son, "but first I must have something to eat."

"Alas!" cried his mother. "I have neither food nor money to buy any."

"Then I will sell the lamp," said Aladdin.

"At least let me polish it," said his mother. "You will get more for it."

As soon as she began to rub it, a great genie appeared and said, "I am the Genie of the Lamp. I serve the one who holds it. What is thy will?"

Aladdin's mother was so frightened that she dropped the lamp. Aladdin snatched it and spoke. "I am hungry. Bring us something to eat."

As Aladdin spoke, the genie disappeared. In a moment he returned with a silver bowl, twelve silver dishes heaped with delicious food, and two silver cups. He placed them on the table and vanished.

"Ah-ha!" said Aladdin. "No wonder my uncle wanted to have this lamp. It can bring me whatever I wish."

As they ate, Aladdin told his mother all that had happened in the cave. She begged him to sell the lamp and have nothing to do with the genie.

"No," said Aladdin. "Since we have learned what it can do, we will use the lamp, and also the ring, which I will always wear on my finger."

The food that the genie had brought lasted a week. When it was gone, Aladdin sold one of the silver plates. And from day to day, as they needed food, he sold the rest of the silver.

When he had nothing more to sell, Aladdin rubbed the lamp again. The genie appeared as before and brought another set of silver dishes heaped with food. Thus Aladdin and his mother were able to live in comfort for many years.

5

One day the Sultan ordered all the people to stay at home and close their shutters, while his daughter, the Princess, passed by on her way to the bath.

Aladdin stayed at home and closed his shutters, but he peeped through them as the Princess was passing. The Princess happened to raise her veil just then, and Aladdin saw her face. The moment he saw her, he loved her with all his heart.

"Mother!" he cried. "I have seen the Princess, and I have made up my mind to marry her. Please go at once to the Sultan and beg him to allow his daughter to marry me."

"What?" cried his mother. "You are mad, my boy. I cannot go to the Sultan."

"Nay, you must go," said Aladdin. "Carry him this basket filled with the fruit that sparkles and shines like the most beautiful jewels. Then he will listen to you."

His mother agreed and went to the palace at once. She waited patiently but no one even spoke to her. She went every day for a week before the Sultan noticed that she was there.

"Who is the poor woman who comes here every day?" he asked. "Bring her forward."

Aladdin's mother knelt before the throne. "Rise, good woman, and tell me what you want," said the Sultan.

She told him of her son's love for the Princess. "He sends you this gift of fruit," she continued, presenting the basket.

"Fruit!" exclaimed the Sultan. "These are diamonds and rubies and sapphires! My daughter may marry one who sends such a gift." Then the Sultan told Aladdin's mother to return in three months' time, when the wedding would take place.

When the time had passed, Aladdin again sent his mother to the Sultan.

"I shall keep my word," said the Sultan, "but he who marries my daughter must first send me forty baskets filled with jewels, like the one you brought before."

Aladdin's mother returned home. "You can never send the gift the Sultan demands," she cried.

"Indeed I can," answered Aladdin. Then he rubbed the lamp. When the genie appeared, Aladdin told him to provide the forty baskets filled with jewels.

When the Sultan received the jewels, he wished Aladdin to marry the Princess without delay. Aladdin was delighted to hear the news. He ordered the genie to bring a purple robe for him to wear, as well as a white horse to ride, and ten thousand gold pieces to give to the people.

At last everything was prepared. Aladdin, dressed in his purple robe, set out for the palace. As he rode along, he scattered gold coins among the people.

At the palace the Sultan greeted Aladdin joyfully and ordered the wedding feast to be prepared at once. "Not so, your majesty," said Aladdin. "I will not marry the Princess until I have built her a palace."

Then he went home and once more rubbed the lamp to call forth the genie. "Build me the finest palace in the world!" ordered Aladdin. "Build it of the finest marble, set with diamonds, rubies, and other precious stones. In the middle you shall build me a large hall with a dome, its four walls of gold and silver, each side having six windows. There must be stables and horses and grooms and servants. Make haste!"

The palace was finished by the next day, and the genie carried him there and showed him all his orders faithfully carried out. The genie had even laid a velvet carpet from Aladdin's palace to the Sultan's.

Aladdin's mother dressed herself carefully and went to the Sultan's palace. She was taken to the Princess, who treated her with great honor. The Princess said goodbye to her father and set out on the carpet for Aladdin's palace, with his mother at her side.

She was charmed at the sight of Aladdin, who ran to greet her.

"Princess," he said, "blame your beauty for my boldness if I have displeased you."

She told him that she willingly obeyed her father in this matter. After the wedding, Aladdin led her into the hall, where a feast was spread. They ate and danced till midnight.

6

For a time Aladdin and the Princess lived happily. Then trouble came to them. The magician was the cause of it. You remember that he was very angry when

Aladdin did not give him the lamp. When the earth had closed over Aladdin, the magician thought, "Well, my lad, we have seen the last of you."

Months had passed and never once did he think of Aladdin. But then, by means of his magic, he learned that the boy had escaped and had married a princess, with whom he was living in great honor and wealth. He knew that the poor tailor's son could only have done this with the help of the Genie of the Lamp.

"I must have that lamp for myself!" cried the magician. At once he dressed himself as a merchant and traveled to the land where Aladdin lived.

When he reached the city where Aladdin lived, he walked up and down the streets. He carried a load of copper lamps. Everywhere he went he cried, "New lamps for old! New lamps for old!"

Now it happened that Aladdin had gone hunting, and the Princess sat alone near an open window. She saw the merchant and sent a servant to find out what the man was calling. The servant came back laughing. "The foolish man says he will give new lamps for old ones!" he said.

The Princess scolded the servant for laughing, and then she pointed to an old lamp. "Take that old lamp," she said, "and see if the man truly wishes to trade it."

When the magician saw the lamp, he knew that it was the one for which he was searching. He took the magic lamp eagerly and gave the servant all the new ones.

Then he hurried out of the city. When he was alone, he rubbed the lamp, and the genie appeared before him.

"What is thy will, master?" said the genie.

"I command you to bring me the Princess and Aladdin's palace, and set us all in a faraway land!" the magician cried. Instantly the palace disappeared.

The next morning, when the Sultan looked out his window, there was no palace to be seen. "This must have been done by magic!" he exclaimed. He sent his soldiers to bring Aladdin home in chains. They met him riding back from the hunt and carried him to the Sultan.

When Aladdin was allowed to speak, he asked, "Why have you made me a prisoner?"

"Wretch!" exclaimed the Sultan. "Come and I will show you." Then he led Aladdin to the window and showed him that where the palace had been, there was now only an empty space.

Aladdin begged the Sultan to grant him forty days in which to seek for the palace and the Princess. On this condition, Aladdin was set free. He searched everywhere, but he could find no trace of the Princess.

In despair, he wrung his hands. As he did so, he rubbed the magic ring. Instantly, the Genie of the Ring appeared.

"I am here, master. What is thy will?" asked the genie.

"Bring back the Princess and the palace," said Aladdin.

"It is not in my power to do that," said the genie. "Only the Genie of the Lamp can bring them back."

"Then take me to the place where the palace now stands and set me down under the window of the Princess."

7

Almost before Aladdin had finished speaking the words, he found himself beneath a window of his own palace.

"Princess! Princess!" he called.

The Princess opened the window. With a cry of joy, Aladdin entered and embraced her. "Tell me," said he, "what has become of the old lamp?"

The Princess shook her head sadly.

"Alas," she sighed, "a man came through the streets crying, 'New lamps for old!' I gave him the old lamp. And the next thing I knew, I was here."

"That man is a cruel magician," said Aladdin. "He has always wished to have the magic lamp. Where is he now?"

"He is still here," said the Princess. "He carries the lamp in his robes during the day, and he places it under his pillow at night."

That night, while the magician was asleep, Aladdin stole softly into the room and took the lamp from under the pillow. Then he rubbed the lamp, and the genie appeared.

"I command you to carry the Princess and the palace back home!" he cried.

The following morning, the Sultan looked out the window. To his surprise, he saw the palace of Aladdin in the very place from which it had vanished.

After that, Aladdin and the Princess lived happily for many years. When the Sultan grew very old and died, they ruled in his place. And they never forgot to guard both the ring and the lamp.

NORSE MYTHS

THE "NORTHMEN" AND THEIR STORIES

Long ago, the people called the Vikings were the masters of the seas. They were sometimes called "Northmen" or "Norsemen," for they came from the northern lands called Scandinavia.

The Vikings were a tough, seafaring people. In their swift longships, they explored lands far from their homes. Often they raided villages and stole whatever they could carry away. The sight of a Viking longship struck fear into the hearts of people who lived in the villages of Europe.

Like the ancient Greeks and Romans before them, the Vikings believed in many different gods, though not the same gods as the Greeks and Romans.

Whenever the Vikings saw a bright rainbow appear in the sky, they would say, "Ah, there is a bridge to Asgard!" They believed Asgard was the land of the gods and goddesses.

Let's learn about some of the Viking gods of Asgard.

Odin was the king of all the gods and goddesses. He shaped the world and set the sun, moon, and stars in their courses. Odin had only one eye. He gave up his other eye so he could drink from a magical spring of wisdom. Once he drank from the spring, he became the wisest god of all.

Thor was Odin's most powerful son. He was the god of thunder and lightning. The Vikings believed that Thor made it thunder when his chariot raced across the sky, and that he caused lightning when he threw his hammer. To the Vikings, red-bearded Thor was a bringer of good luck. Many Vikings even carried small charms in the shape of a hammer for good luck.

Gentle Freya was the goddess of love and beauty. She usually wore a necklace and took the form of a bird when she traveled.

Tyr was the Viking god of war, but he was not hotheaded or angry. He was wise and brave. Warriors prayed to Tyr and carved his name onto their swords and axes.

Did you know that some days of the week are named after Viking gods?

Tuesday is named after Tyr, the Viking god of war. Our word, Tuesday, comes from "Tyr's Day."

Wednesday is named for the king of the Viking gods, Odin. Some people called him "Woden," and so from "Woden's Day" we get the name Wednesday.

If you hear thunder on Thursday, remember that Thursday is "Thor's Day." And Friday is "Freya's Day."

The Vikings believed in other gods, too. One of them was called Loki. He was a god who was always making mischief.

The Vikings told many stories about their gods and goddesses. We no longer believe these myths, but we still enjoy reading them because they are such interesting stories.

LOKI AND THE DWARFS

1

Loki was the god of fire. He was very mischievous, and he was always playing tricks on other gods.

One day, as he was walking idly through the city of Asgard, he came to the palace of Thor, the god of thunder, and strongest of all the gods. On the steps of the palace sat Sif, Thor's wife, fast asleep. Her long hair fell about her and shone like gold in the sunshine.

When Loki saw the long golden hair, a thrill of mischief ran through him. "I'll cut it off while she sleeps," he thought, "and she'll never know who did it."

So he stole up softly behind Sif as she sat asleep and cut off every bit of her hair. Then he ran away, for at any moment Thor might return and find who had done it. Loki knew very well that he could expect no mercy from Thor.

After a while Sif woke up and, finding all her hair gone, she cried and cried. At last she hid herself, for she wanted no one to see her.

In a little while Thor came home. With many tears, Sif told him the terrible story—that she had fallen asleep on the steps of the palace, and that while she slept someone had cut off her hair.

As she talked, Thor grew more and more angry. "I know who did it!" he shouted. "It was that rascal Loki. I'll find him and make him put every hair back on your head." And off he rushed to find Loki, who by this time was very much afraid.

It was not long before Thor found Loki trying to hide. He seized him hard around the throat.

"You villain!" he thundered. "Put back the hair on Sif's head."

"Let me go!" cried Loki. "I can't put back Sif's hair. You know I can't."

"Yes, you can," said Thor. "You must. Promise you will do it."

Loki was very much afraid of Thor, so he promised. "I'll find some way to do it," he said, "only stop choking me."

After Loki had sworn to restore Sif's hair, Thor let him go.

Loki was a great friend of the dwarfs, who lived far under the ground. These dwarfs were cunning jewelers, and they were busy all day long making wonderful things of gold and silver. So Loki paid them a visit.

"Dwarfs," he said, "make me a crown of golden hair that will grow like real hair, and I will give you anything you want for your trouble."

"Very well," replied the dwarfs.

To make magic hair that would grow on Sif's head was a very simple matter for such clever workers. Soon the hair was ready, shining and smooth and soft. Besides the hair, the dwarfs also made for Loki a ship and a golden spear.

The ship was not like any you have ever seen or will see. It was a magic ship that could be taken apart and folded small enough to go in one's pocket. When it was put together and placed in the water, it grew and grew till it was large enough to hold a great army. And besides, it could sail just as well without wind as with it. That was the best part of the charm.

The golden spear was also made with magic. When thrown, it never missed the mark. A very fine spear it was, and Loki was glad to have it.

He thanked the dwarfs and began to climb up out of the cave to the sunshine. But just at the gate he met the dwarf called Brok of the Big Head because his head was quite the largest part of him.

"Hello, Loki!" said Brok. "What have you there?"

"Three great treasures which the dwarfs have made for me," replied Loki proudly.

"Poof," said Brok. "Those are merely toys. You should see what my brother Sind can do."

Loki showed Brok his precious gifts. "There!" he said. "Can your brother Sind do better than that?"

Brok laughed and nodded his big head. "Give him two days, Loki, and I will bring to the city three treasures far greater than these. The gods shall decide whether your dwarfs can do better than my brother Sind. If you win, you shall cut off my head. If I win, I will cut off yours."

"Agreed," said Loki.

2

When the two days were over, Loki and Brok went to Asgard, each carrying his wonderful gifts. There they found the gods sitting in the great hall. Odin, Thor, his wife Sif, and all the others were seated on their golden thrones.

Loki bowed low before them. "O gods," he said, "Brok and I have each brought three gifts, and you are to decide which you like the better. If I lose, this dwarf is to cut off my head."

Loki first brought out the magic spear which could never miss its mark. This he gave to Odin, who hurled it and said, "Good! Very good, indeed, brother!"

The golden hair he gave to Thor, who at once placed it on Sif's head, where it began to grow just like any other hair. Sif was delighted with her new hair and forgave Loki for the mischief he had done.

Then Loki took out the ship, all folded like a toy boat. He told them that it was a magic ship, and that when placed in the water it would grow and grow till it was large enough to carry many people, and that besides this it could go without any breeze. This he gave to Freya, and you cannot imagine how pleased Freya was with this gift.

"Well done!" said all the gods, and Loki smiled proudly.

It was now Brok's turn.

"Surely you cannot show us anything better than Loki's gifts," said Odin. "But come, let us see what you have brought."

Then Brok of the Big Head brought a big bag to the foot of the throne. "You shall soon see," he said.

First he pulled out a ring of gold, which he gave to Odin. "This," he said, "is a magic ring. Every ninth day there will drop from it nine other rings just like it."

"Well done, Brok of the Big Head!" Odin cried, and all the gods clapped their hands.

Once more Brok stooped to the big bag. "I give you," he said to Freya, "this gold boar. He is a magic boar and can run faster than any horse. Besides, his bristles are like stars and on the darkest night you will need no lantern."

"That is a fine gift," said Freya. "I can ride about the world faster on this boar than on my horse. Loki, this is better than your boat."

Then Brok drew out of the bag the third gift. It was a hammer. "This," said the dwarf, "is a magic hammer. It will break the strongest iron. And no matter how far or how hard you throw it, it will always come back to you. Besides, you can make it very little to put into your pocket. I give it to Thor."

The gods were so pleased with the dwarf's gifts that they declared he had won the wager. So Loki was to lose his head.

"Brok," said Loki, "I will give you anything you wish in exchange for my head."

But Brok refused.

"Well then," said Loki, "catch me if you can." And away he went like the wind, for Loki had on magic shoes.

Brok was angry. He stamped about and tore his hair with rage. He turned to Freya, to whom he had given the magic boar. "Catch him," he begged. "I gave you the magic boar. Ride after him and bring him back."

Freya mounted the boar and soon brought Loki back.

"So," said Brok, " I shall have your head after all."

"You said my head and not my neck," said Loki. "You may have my head but not one inch of my neck."

"That is so," said the gods.

Brok was puzzled, for how could he cut off Loki's head without touching his neck? If he touched Loki's neck, he knew the gods would punish him severely for it. He thought for a long time.

"After all," he growled, "I don't want your head. But I am going to sew up your boasting lips."

So with a stout needle and a strong thread he sewed up Loki's lips, and the mischievous god was unable for a long time to set them free. During that time he could carry no tales, and this saved the other gods from much trouble and sorrow.

THE MAGIC APPLES

1

Once upon a time Odin and Loki started on a journey together. They traveled all day through a lonely country, where neither a house nor a person was to be seen.

"We must soon come to a house," said Odin, "and perhaps the people will give us some dinner."

The sun sank low in the sky, but still there was no house to be seen, and there was not even a berry or a nut to pick by the way. They felt as if they were starving, when from the top of a high hill they saw a herd of cattle.

"See!" cried Loki. "There is our dinner."

They ran down the hill into the meadow and caught one of the cattle. In a very short time they had a fine dinner roasting over a great fire. Then they sat down to wait.

"Our dinner must be done now," said Loki after a long while.

But no. It was not nearly done. Another half hour went by, but the meat was as raw as ever.

"What can be the matter?" asked Loki. "This meat must have some magic charm upon it."

Just then a voice came from the oak tree over their heads. They looked up and saw sitting in the tree a great eagle, larger than any bird they had ever seen before. There he sat staring at them.

"What is the matter with your dinner?" asked the eagle. "You must be very bad cooks. Give me a share, and I'll soon have your dinner ready for you."

"By all means," said Loki.

So the eagle flew down, and in a very short time had the dinner ready.

"Now take your share," said Odin. He thought that a small piece would be enough. But the eagle was hungry. He seized a leg and both shoulders, and started to fly away.

"Stop, thief!" cried Loki. "That is more than your share. You did not earn that. Drop it, I say." And taking a pole, he began to swing at the eagle.

Then a strange thing happened. One end of the pole stuck to the eagle's back, and Loki was not able to let go of the other end.

Away flew the eagle, now high, now low, screaming with delight.

"Stop! Stop!" cried Loki. But the eagle flew on, dragging him through bushes and briers, over trees and rocks and hills, till Loki thought he should die.

"Ha, Loki!" the eagle laughed. "You cannot get away unless I say so. You are under a spell, but I will let you go if you will do one thing for me."

Poor Loki was so sore and bruised that he was ready to agree to anything.

"Listen carefully, Loki," said the eagle. "I am really a frost giant, and I want the magic apples that the gods eat to keep from growing old. Promise to get them for me and I will let you go."

These apples were magic apples, as the giant had said. They were very beautiful to look at, but the best thing about them was that whoever ate one became young again.

Loki replied, "You know that they are the most precious things in all Asgard. How in the world can I get them?"

"Steal them," said the eagle gruffly.

"That would be impossible," said Loki. "They are too carefully guarded. Idun has nothing to do but take care of the basket in which the apples are kept. One cry from her, and all Asgard would fly to help her."

"Where are your clever ways, Loki?" asked the eagle. "Come—you must coax Idun outside of the city gates, then I will carry her away, apples and all. You need not do anything more. Promise, and I will let you go."

Loki thought and thought. "Let me go," he said at last. "Within a week you will find Idun with the apples outside the city gates."

The eagle flew down and gently dropped Loki on a soft bed of moss.

2

One day after the eagle had released Loki, he went to see Idun as she was putting away her apples in the beautiful basket in which she kept them. "Good morning, fair Idun," said Loki politely. "How beautiful your apples are!"

"Yes," said Idun, "they are beautiful. They are the most beautiful apples in the world."

"I don't know about that," said Loki. "I have seen some even more beautiful."

"I do not believe you!" cried Idun.

"Well," said Loki, "I can show them to you. The apples I saw were larger and sweeter than yours."

"I do not believe you," said Idun again. "Still," she added, "I should like to see them. Where are they?"

"Outside the gates of the city," said Loki. "They grow on a little tree in the woods."

"Please take me to see them, Loki," said Idun. "Is it very far?"

So they started off together, Idun carrying the golden basket that held her magic apples. They had just stepped outside the gates when, with a great whirring of wings, down came the mighty eagle. He fastened his claws in Idun's belt and flew away with her to the land of giants.

Loki went back to the city, thinking that no one would ever find out about this new piece of mischief.

At first the gods did not miss Idun, but as the days went by and there were no magic apples to make them feel young, they began to be alarmed. After a time their alarm turned to terror. Their hair was beginning to grow white, and they began to move about slowly like old people.

Finally they held a council to find out who had last seen Idun. They found that Loki had been seen with her strolling in the direction of the city gates. "Ah," said the gods, "now we understand."

Loki was caught and bound and brought before the council. "Tell us the truth," they said, "or die."

Loki was so frightened that he told all about his promise to the giant.

"Alas! What shall we do?" wailed the gods. "Idun is stolen away, and we are growing old." The gods were so angry that they were going to kill Loki at once. But Odin said, "Bring Idun back from the land of the giants, and you may live."

"How shall I do that?" asked Loki.

"How do I know?" returned Odin. "That is for you to find out."

For a moment Loki thought, and then he said, "Give me the dress of a falcon, and I will bring her back."

So the gods gave him the dress of a falcon, and when he had put it on, he flew away.

He traveled for many days, till at last he saw before him the great ice palace of the frost giant. He questioned the birds that he met in the woods nearby, and they told him that the giant had gone hunting. "Ah," said Loki, "now is the time to take Idun home."

When he reached the castle, he hopped upon a windowsill and looked in. There was poor Idun, weeping for her home in Asgard. She heard the flapping of the wings and looked up.

"Idun, it is I, Loki," said the falcon. "Come along. I have come to take you home."

Idun stopped crying and seized the basket of apples. "I am ready," she said. "But how shall I get out? The door is locked and the window is barred."

"I'll change you into a nut," said Loki. "I will carry you in one claw and the basket of apples in the other."

He did so and off they started.

It was not long before the giant came home. Finding Idun and her apples gone, he put on his eagle dress and flew after them.

Now an eagle is much larger than a falcon and can fly much more swiftly. So it was not long before Loki heard the scream of the eagle behind him. He flew faster and faster over mountains and rivers and forests, but nearer and nearer came the eagle.

The gods were all upon the walls of the city watching eagerly. They held their breath when they saw the eagle chasing the falcon. They were afraid that the falcon would not be able to reach Asgard.

Some of the gods built great fires all around the city walls. Then they waited. Just as the eagle was ready to pounce upon him, the falcon made one last effort. He passed through the fire and over the wall.

The eagle tried to follow. But frost giants cannot pass through fire. Loki, Idun, and the golden apples were all beyond his reach.

Then the gods gathered around the magic apples, and as they ate, they became young once more.

SIGURD AND THE DRAGON

Long ago, the Northmen say, there lived a brave prince named Sigurd. Sigurd had a noble heart. He faced terrible danger to help those in need, and by his great deeds, he earned himself a place among the heroes of the earth.

One morning, a man burst into Sigurd's palace. His clothes were in tatters, and he was dusted from head to toe with thick, white ash. "Prince Sigurd," he cried, "help us, please!"

"Sit, my good man," said Sigurd, "and take food and drink before you tell me your tale."

"Good prince," gasped the man, "there is no time. I come to you from the Glittering Heath. Do you know the land?"

"Indeed I do," replied Sigurd. "It is a fair land of green fields and busy villages, from the wide, blue river to the snow-capped mountains."

"Ah! That was once my home," sobbed the man. "But, my prince, you would no longer know the place. The land is cold and silent. Once the trees raised their leafy branches to touch the clouds. But now, only blasted splinters litter the dull earth. Once the larkspur winked its blue eye at the smiling sun. But now, an icy, wet ash covers all. And woe to those who stray within, for he who goes into the Glittering Heath never comes out again!"

"By the gods of Asgard," cried Sigurd, "what has brought such trouble upon you?"

The man trembled, as though the tale were too awful to tell. With great effort he whispered, "An evil shadow has covered the land. It came with a beating of fell wings. Oh, good prince, a terrible dragon is ravaging our fair countryside. He has wiped out whole villages with one swipe of his tail. He has destroyed a dozen fields with one mouthful of his poisonous breath. He has seized all the gold and treasure he can find. He has piled it into a great heap, and coiled himself around it. Night and day, he guards it without sleeping."

Sigurd shouted quick orders for his armor, his sword, and his horse. Then he said to the poor man, "Be at peace. I promise you, I will not return until the dragon is dead and the Glittering Heath is safe."

Sigurd rode until he reached the river that bordered the Glittering Heath. The cold, murky waters smelled of decay. Sigurd's horse whinnied and refused to step into the water.

As Sigurd wondered how he might cross the river, a boat sailed silently out of the mist. The boatman called out, "What man are you who dares to enter the Glittering Heath?"

"I am Sigurd," answered the prince, "and I have come to slay the dragon."

"Then come into my boat," replied the boatman. "I will carry you across the river."

Sigurd stepped into the boat. Without oars or even a breath of wind, the little boat turned around and began to cross the river.

The boatman drew his deep blue hood down over his face and asked, "How will you fight the dragon, young prince?"

"I will slay him with my sword," replied Sigurd.

The boatman laughed softly, making the golden stars on his cloak seem to dance. "But the dragon breathes poisons, his eyes shoot lightning, and he is stronger than ten heroes," he said.

"I am not afraid," replied Sigurd.

"Then be wise, and listen to me," said the boatman. "You will need all your strength to slay the beast, but you will need to use it wisely."

Sigurd wondered at the mysterious boatman. From under his dark hood, there seemed to gleam but one shining eye. "What would you have me do?" asked Sigurd.

"Follow the trail over the Glittering Heath," said the boatman. "Every day the dragon comes down from his pile of gold and follows that trail to drink at the river. Dig a pit in the trail and hide in it. In the morning, when the dragon passes over you, leap forth and plunge your sword into his heart."

The boat bumped against the shore and Sigurd jumped out. But when he turned to thank the boatman, both the boatman and the boat had disappeared. Sigurd remembered that the boatman had worn a blue hood spangled with golden stars, and that his one eye shone with a strange light. Then Sigurd knew he had spoken with Odin, the king of the gods.

With new courage, Sigurd found the dragon's trail, dug a pit, and lay down in it to wait for morning.

He did not wait long. At first light, the dragon shook himself awake and raced down the muddy trail. Sigurd looked out of the pit. He saw the enormous, scaly body, the long teeth, and the eyes filled with hatred. He saw the sharp, curved claws that dug deep into the cracked earth. With each flap of its batlike wings, the monster knocked down dead trees like toothpicks.

Sigurd waited in the pit. His sword shone brightly in the morning light. When the dragon's inky body rolled over him, Sigurd struck.

The earth shook with the fury of the dragon's roar. The beast rose up on his hind legs, blocking out the sun, clawing the air as if he would tear open the sky. Each beat of his thick, black wings sent howling winds swirling around Sigurd. The air filled with white ash that burned and stung all it touched. But Sigurd's sword had pierced the dragon's heart, and soon the monster dropped dead upon the earth.

Even as the dragon fell, a shadow seemed to lift from the land. The golden rays of the sun bathed all in warm light. Trees grew up out of the bare ground, flowers blossomed, and the river ran clear and bright.

Sigurd's horse galloped to his side and neighed joyfully. "Yes, my friend," said Sigurd, "now the Glittering Heath glitters once again. But let us leave behind this beast and his ill-gotten gold. For the day is not far off when we shall do even greater deeds than this."

TALES OF HANS CHRISTIAN ANDERSEN

HANS CHRISTIAN ANDERSEN

Hans Christian Andersen was born in Denmark. He spent his boyhood in the little village of Odense. His father and mother were very poor. The family lived in two little rooms near the top of a house, where the father worked as a shoemaker.

On the roof of the house was a box filled with earth. In this box, his mother planted her vegetables.

Little Hans loved to walk with his father in the woods, where he could gather wild flowers and hear the birds sing. His father read to him when his work was done, or told him stories.

When Hans was a little fellow, he went into a wheat field with his mother and some other children to gather the wheat the reapers had left in the field. While they were busy gathering their little handfuls, an angry bailiff came rushing into the field, armed with a whip. All ran away from the angry man as fast as they could. But little Hans was barefooted, and the sharp stubble cut his feet so that he could not get away.

Unafraid, the lad faced the angry man with the whip. "How dare you strike me when you know God sees you?" he cried, looking fearlessly into the face of the furious bailiff.

The bailiff brought down the whip, but not on little Hans. He admired the lad's courage, and praised him for it, and sent him home with gifts rather than blows.

While Hans was still a boy, his kind father died. Then Hans and his mother were left alone to care for each other.

"What will you do, Hans?" his mother asked. "Would you like to become a tailor?"

"No, mother," the boy answered. "I will go to Copenhagen and study. Some day I shall write books."

"But where will the money be found to pay your way?" asked the mother.

"I will work, and God will take care of me," Hans replied.

So the boy left his native village and walked all the long way to Copenhagen.

Some day you may read the story of his life in the great city. The poor, homeless boy worked and suffered for many months. At last a kind man heard of this lad who loved stories and who told them so well that his hearers wept or laughed with him. After reading a story Hans had written, he said to the lad, "I will send you to school, and you shall be cared for until you have learned to write as you wish."

That was a glad day for Hans Christian Andersen. At school he toiled with all his might and all his heart. At night he slept in a tiny attic room. From the windows he could see only the house walls and chimneys. But when he looked up, he met the gaze of the moon and the stars.

As he grew older, he wrote many stories for children. Perhaps you know some of the stories he wrote, such as "The Ugly Duckling" or "The Princess and the Pea." Children in every land came to love his stories and think of this writer as their friend.

Hans Christian Andersen became so famous and well-loved that the people of Denmark had a beautiful statue carved in his honor. They placed it in the king's garden, where the children played. The statue shows Andersen telling a story to a group of children.

When the statue was first shown, they made a great holiday upon his birthday. Letters and gifts came from all his friends, including the king himself. That was a happy day for the children's friend.

The Emperor's New Clothes

1

Many years ago there lived an emperor who was so fond of fancy new clothes that he spent all his money on them. He did not care about his soldiers, or the theater, or driving about in his coach, unless it was to show off his new clothes. He had different robes for every hour of the day.

In the great city in which he lived it was always merry. Strangers were always coming and going.

One day two rogues came. They said they were weavers. They declared they could weave the finest cloth anyone could imagine, with beautiful colors and patterns. They also said that any clothes made of this cloth were so fine that they could not be seen by anyone who was unfit for his job, or who was very stupid.

"Those would be wonderful clothes!" thought the emperor. "If I wore those, I would be able to find out which men in my empire are not fit for the jobs they have. I could tell the clever ones from the dunces. Yes, that cloth must be woven for me right away!"

Then he gave the two rogues a great deal of money and told them to begin their work at once.

So these two swindlers put up two looms and pretended to be working. But they had nothing at all on their looms. They asked for the finest silk and the finest gold thread from which to weave the cloth. They put these things away for themselves, and they worked at their empty looms till late at night.

"I would like to know how much they have finished," thought the emperor. But he felt quite uncomfortable when he thought that those who were not fit for their jobs could not see the cloth. He believed that he had nothing to fear for himself. Still, he wanted first to send someone else to see how things were going.

"I will send my honest old advisor to the weavers," thought the emperor. "He can judge best how the stuff looks, for he has sense, and no one is more fit for his job."

Now the good old advisor went out into the hall, where the two rogues sat working at the empty looms.

"Mercy on me!" thought the old advisor, and he opened his eyes wide. "I cannot see anything at all!"

But he did not say this.

Both the rogues begged him to come nearer. They asked if he liked the colors and the pattern. Then they pointed to the empty loom. The poor old advisor went on opening his eyes wide, but he could see nothing, for there was nothing to see.

"Mercy!" he thought. "Can I indeed be so stupid? Am I not fit for my job? No, it will never do for me to say that I cannot see the cloth."

"Have you nothing to say about our work?" asked one swindler as he went on pretending to weave.

"Oh, it is charming—yes, quite enchanting!" answered the old advisor as he peered through his spectacles. "What a fine pattern, and what colors! Yes, I shall tell the emperor that I am very much pleased with it."

"Well, we are glad of that," said the weavers. Then they named the colors and explained the curious patterns in the cloth. The old advisor listened with attention, so that he might be able to repeat it when the emperor came.

Now the rogues said they needed more money, and more silk and gold, to finish their weaving. They put it all into their own pockets. Not a thread was put on the looms. They went on working on the empty looms as before.

The emperor sent a second messenger to see if the cloth would soon be ready. The same thing happened to him. He looked and looked, but as there was nothing to see but the empty looms, he could see nothing.

"Isn't this a beautiful piece of material?" asked the two rogues, as they displayed and explained the handsome pattern, which was not there at all.

"I am not stupid!" thought the man. "Am I not fit for my job? That may be, but no one shall find out!" And so he praised the cloth that he did not see, and expressed his pleasure at the beautiful colors and pleasing pattern. "Yes, it is lovely," he told the emperor.

2

All the people were talking of the beautiful cloth. And now the emperor wished to see it for himself while it was still on the loom.

With a crowd of chosen men, among whom were the two gentlemen who had already been there, he went to the two cunning rogues. They were now weaving with might and main, but without fiber or thread.

"Isn't it splendid?" said the two men who had already been there. "Does not your majesty admire the pattern and the colors?" And they pointed to the empty loom, for they thought the others could see the cloth.

"What's this?" thought the emperor. "I can see nothing at all! This is terrible. Am I stupid? Am I not fit to be an emperor? That would be the most dreadful thing that could happen to me."

But aloud he said, "Oh, it is very pretty! It meets with my approval." And he nodded in a contented way, and gazed at the empty loom, for he would not say that he saw nothing.

The whole group with him looked and looked, and saw nothing more than the rest. But, like the emperor, they said, "Yes, it's very pretty!" Then they advised him to wear an outfit made from the splendid new cloth at the great parade that was very soon to take place.

The whole night before the morning of the parade, the rogues were up. They kept more than sixteen candles burning. The people could see that they were hard at work, finishing the emperor's new clothes. They pretended to take the stuff down from the loom.

They made cuts in the air with sharp scissors. They sewed with needles without thread. And at last they said, "Now the clothes are ready!"

The emperor came with his noblest gentlemen. The two rogues lifted up one arm as if they were holding something, and said, "See, here is the cloak! It is as light as a spider's web. One would think one had nothing on. But that is just the beauty of it."

"Yes," said all the gentlemen. But they could not see anything, for nothing was there.

"Will your royal majesty now kindly consent to take off your robe?" said the rogues. "Then we will put on your new clothes here in front of the great mirror."

The emperor took off his robe. The rogues pretended to put on him each new garment as it was ready. The emperor turned round and round before the mirror.

"Oh, how well they look! How very well they fit!" said all. "What a pattern! What colors! That is a splendid robe!"

At that moment the master of ceremonies announced, "Your majesty, they are standing outside and ready to begin the parade!"

"Well, I am ready," replied the emperor. "Does it not suit me well?" And he turned again to look in the mirror.

The two noblemen who were to carry the flowing train of the emperor's robe stooped down and fumbled about on the floor. Then they pretended to be holding something in the air. They did not dare to admit that they saw nothing.

So the emperor walked forth, and everyone said, "How wonderful are the emperor's new clothes! How well they fit!" No one would let it appear that he could see nothing, for that would have shown that he was not fit for his job, or was very stupid.

But then a little child said, "But he hasn't got any clothes on!"

"Hear what the little one says!" said the child's father, and one person whispered to another what the child had said.

"But he hasn't got any clothes on!" said all the people at last. A strange feeling passed over the emperor as he began to think that the people were right.

But he thought to himself, "I must go on." And so he held himself a little higher, and the noblemen held on tighter than ever, and carried the train that was not there at all.

— Hans Christian Andersen

THE EMPEROR AND THE NIGHTINGALE

1

A great many years ago, the Emperor of China lived in a palace made of the finest porcelain. It was so delicate that it could be touched only with the greatest care. In the Emperor's garden grew the most amazing flowers. The garden was so big that even the gardener himself did not know where it ended. It stretched on and on, through lofty woods and deep lakes to the deep blue sea.

Among the trees lived a nightingale. This bird's song was so sweet that even the tired fisherman, who had much work to do, would stop pulling his nets to listen.

Travelers from many countries came to visit the Emperor. They admired his palace. They enjoyed walking in his gardens. But when they heard the nightingale sing, they said, "Ah! That is finer than anything."

Some of the travelers went home and wrote books about the palace and the gardens. Some wrote books with poems about the nightingale in the woods by the deep blue sea.

One of these books reached the Emperor. He was pleased to read such warm words about his palace and gardens. Then he read about the little nightingale in his garden and her wonderful songs.

"How is this?" said the Emperor. "Have I such a wonderful bird as this in my own garden and have never seen it or heard it?"

So he had his first lord-in-waiting called before him.

"Why have I never seen nor heard the nightingale in my garden?" asked the Emperor. "In the books they say it is better than anything else in my kingdom."

But the first lord-in-waiting was a silly man who had never been in the garden in his life. He knew nothing about the nightingale. "Your majesty must not believe everything that is written in books," he said to the Emperor.

But the Emperor insisted. "I will hear this nightingale. Go and seek her at once," he commanded. "When you have found her, invite her politely to come to court and sing for me."

The first lord-in-waiting hurried away, but he did not know where in the world to look. So he asked everybody he met to show him the nightingale. But no one had ever seen her.

At last, the first lord-in-waiting went where he had never been before—into the kitchen. There he found a poor little maid washing dishes who knew something about the nightingale.

"Oh, yes, indeed," said the little kitchen-maid. "I hear the nightingale almost every night when I take the leftover food to my poor sick mother who lives near the shore. On my way back, I stop to rest in the woods, and then I hear the nightingale. Her song brings tears to my eyes. I can point her out to you." She led the way out into the garden.

They had gone only a little way when they heard something lowing in the distance. "Ah, yes," said the lord-in-waiting. "That must be the nightingale. How sweetly she sings!"

"That is only a cow," said the little kitchen-maid. So they went on. Soon they heard something croaking.

"There!" said the lord-in-waiting. "There is the nightingale. How sweetly she sings!"

"That is only frogs!" said the little kitchen-maid. "But hark now! There she is!" They crept softly to where the little gray bird sat singing to the moon.

"Is it possible?" said the lord-in-waiting. "It looks so plain and common."

"Dear nightingale," said the little kitchen-maid, "the Emperor wishes you to come and sing before him."

"My song sounds best among the trees," said the nightingale. But she went with them willingly because the Emperor wished it.

2

At the palace, the nightingale sang so charmingly for the Emperor that tears ran down his face. He wished to give her his golden slipper as a reward. But the nightingale said no, for an Emperor's tears were reward enough.

And now the nightingale would stay at the palace and sing to the Emperor every day. She had a gold cage. She could fly into the garden, but only with a silken thread tied to her foot. It was not a pleasant life for the nightingale.

One day, someone sent the Emperor a package. On the outside was written the word *Nightingale*.

"Ah!" said the Emperor. "Here is another book about our wonderful bird." But it was not a book. It was a golden bird all covered with rubies, pearls, and diamonds. When it was wound up, the bird could sing one song.

"Let us have the two birds sing together," said everyone. So the birds sang at the same time. But of course they did not sound well together. Each time, the real nightingale sang a new song in its own way, while the golden bird sang the same tune over and over.

The golden bird was so much prettier to look at that everyone said she sang better. The poor fisherman, however, said, "It sounds very nice, but there is something missing."

Then they looked round for the real nightingale. But she was gone. She had flown quietly out the window and gone back to live in the garden.

"What a most ungrateful bird!" the people cried.

The golden bird was placed on a silken pillow by the Emperor's bed. Gold and jewels were placed around it.

Sometimes the golden bird was brought out for the people to hear. After hearing the song many times, the people knew it by heart. For this they liked the bird even better, for they could join in the song themselves.

Things went on this way for a year. Then one evening, while the Emperor was lying in bed listening to the golden bird, a spring inside snapped and the singing stopped.

The Emperor sent for his best doctors, but what could they do? Finally, a watchmaker got the bird to work again. But then they only dared to let it sing once a year.

3

Five years went by. The Emperor became very sick. He lay cold and pale in his royal bed. His people thought him dead, and they all ran away to greet the next Emperor. Through all the palace not a person was seen. Not a step was heard in the halls. All was silent and deserted.

A window stood open by the Emperor. The moon shone in upon him and upon the little gold bird by his bed.

The poor Emperor could scarcely breathe for a heavy weight on his chest. He opened his eyes and saw Death sitting on his chest. Death had put on the Emperor's golden crown. He held in one hand the Emperor's golden sword and in the other the Emperor's glorious banner. He was sure the Emperor would die.

All around the bed and peeping through the long velvet curtains were a number of faces, some ugly and some pleasant. These were the Emperor's good and bad deeds. They had come to stare him in the face now that Death sat on his heart.

"Do you recall this? Do you remember this? Do you recall me?" they asked the poor Emperor one after another.

"I do not know anything about you!" cried the Emperor. "Music! Music to drown them out! Let the royal band strike up!"

But no one came to answer him. And the faces came and went before the Emperor as before, while Death nodded to all they said.

"Music!" cried the Emperor faintly. "You little golden bird, sing! I have given you gold and jewels. Now when I need you, sing!" But the bird remained silent. There was no one to wind it up.

Death continued to stare at the Emperor with his hollow eyes, and the room was fearfully still.

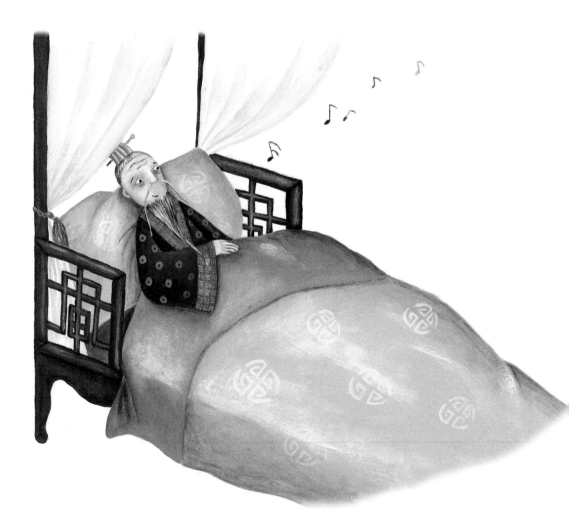

Suddenly, there came through the window a burst of lovely song. Outside on the branch of a tree sat the little gray nightingale.

She had heard that the Emperor was sick. She had come to sing to him of hope and trust. And as she sang, the shadows grew paler and paler. The Emperor's blood began to run faster and give him new life.

Even Death listened. At last, Death rose slowly

from the Emperor's chest and floated out of the window like a white mist.

"Thank you! Oh, thank you! I know you well, you heavenly little bird!" cried the sick Emperor. "I once slighted you for that little gold thing over there. Yet you have come back to drive Death from my heart."

"Think no more of that," said the little gray nightingale. "But sleep now and grow strong while I sing."

The Emperor fell into a sweet sleep from which he awoke almost well. The sun was shining in his room. But no one had returned and he was alone except for the nightingale outside the window.

"You must stay with me, dear bird," said the Emperor.

"I cannot live in the palace and build my nest," said the nightingale. "But I will come every evening and sing to you. I will sing to you of joy and happiness. I will tell you of all in your kingdom who are happy or who suffer. I will sing of all the evil and good around you. I will sing to you of the poor fisherman and the little kitchen-maid and the many who are so far from your way of life. But you must promise me one thing."

"Everything!" cried the Emperor.

"Just one thing," said the bird. "Let no one know that you have a little bird who tells you everything." With that, the nightingale flew away into the garden.

Just then the lord-in-waiting and others came in to see their dead Emperor—and there he stood, greeting them with a hearty "Good morning!"

– Hans Christian Andersen

THE LITTLE MATCH GIRL

On the last evening of the old year, it was terribly cold and nearly dark. The snow was falling fast. In the cold and the darkness, a poor little girl with bare head and naked feet roamed through the streets.

She had worn a pair of slippers when she left home, but they were not of much use. They had belonged to her mother. They were so large that the poor little girl had lost them in running across the street to avoid the carriages. One of the slippers she could not find. A boy seized upon the other and ran away with it. So the little girl went on, her little naked feet blue with the cold.

In an old apron she carried a number of matches. She had a bundle of them in her hands. No one had bought any matches from her the whole day, nor had anyone given her even a penny. She crept along, shivering with cold and hunger. The snowflakes fell on her hair and shoulders.

Lights were shining from every window, and there was a fine smell of roast goose in the air. So she remembered that it was New Year's Eve. In a corner between two houses, she sank down and huddled herself together.

She had drawn her little feet under her, but she could not keep off the cold. And she dared not go home, for she had sold no matches. She had not even a penny of money to take home. Her father would certainly beat her. Besides, it was almost as cold at home as here, for they had only the roof to cover them, and the wind howled through it, although the largest holes had been stopped up with straw and rags.

Her little hands were almost frozen. Perhaps a burning match might do some good, if she could draw it from the bundle and strike it against the wall just to warm her fingers. She drew one out—*scratch*! How it sputtered as it burned. It gave a warm, bright light, like a little candle, as she held her hand over it.

It was really a wonderful light. It seemed to the little girl that she was sitting by a large iron stove. How the fire burned! It seemed so warm that she stretched out her feet as if to warm them. But then the flame of the match went out, the stove vanished, and she had only the half-burned match in her hand.

She rubbed another match on the wall. It burst into a flame. Where its light fell, the wall became as thin as a veil, and she could see into a room of the house. The table was covered with a snowy-white tablecloth. On it was a steaming roast goose, stuffed with apples and dried plums. And, still more wonderful, the goose jumped down from the dish and waddled across the floor, carrying a knife and fork, straight to the little girl!

Then the match went out, and there remained nothing but the thick, damp, cold wall before her.

She lighted another match, and then she found herself sitting under a beautiful Christmas tree. Thousands of lights were burning upon the green branches. The little girl stretched out her hand toward them, and the match went out.

The Christmas lights rose higher and higher, till they looked to her like the stars in the sky. Then she saw a star fall, leaving behind it a bright streak of fire.

"Someone is dying," thought the little girl. Her old grandmother, the only one who had ever loved her, and who was now dead, had told her that when a star falls, a soul is going up to heaven.

She again rubbed a match on the wall, and the light shone round her. In the brightness stood her old grandmother, clear and shining, yet kind and loving, in her appearance.

"Grandmother!" cried the little one. "Oh, take me with you! I know you will go away when the match burns out. You will vanish like the warm stove, the roast goose, and the beautiful Christmas tree." And she hurried to light the whole bundle of matches, for she wished to keep her grandmother there.

The matches glowed with a light that was brighter than the noonday, and her grandmother appeared more beautiful than ever. She took the little girl in her arms, and they both flew upward in brightness and joy, far above the earth, where there was neither cold, nor hunger, nor pain.

In the dawn of the morning, there lay the poor little girl, with pale cheeks and smiling mouth, leaning against the wall. She had frozen to death on the last evening of the old year. Now the new year's sun rose and shone upon her. The child still sat, in the stiffness of death, holding the burned bundle of matches in her hand.

"She tried to warm herself," said someone. But no one imagined what beautiful things she had seen, nor into what glory she had entered with her grandmother, on New Year's Day.

– Hans Christian Andersen

POETRY

VOYAGES

BEYOND THE BROOK

There's a brook in the meadow back of the house,
　　A brook that is deep and wide—
So wide that I know I never can cross,
　　And play on the other side.

The sun always shines on the other bank,
　　And the grass is soft and green;
I know that the apples that grow on those trees
　　Are the sweetest that ever were seen.

The children who live there may play all day,
　　And they always have cakes for tea.
I never have been there, but this is true,
　　For a little bird told it to me.

So I wish that I were a giant tall,
　　And traveled a mile at a stride;
Then I'd cross the brook, and see for myself
　　What lies on the other side.

– Margaret J. McElroy

THE LAND OF NOD

From breakfast on through all the day
At home among my friends I stay,
But every night I go abroad
Afar into the land of Nod.

All by myself I have to go,
With none to tell me what to do—
All alone beside the streams
And up the mountainsides of dreams.

The strangest things are there for me,
Both things to eat and things to see,
And many frightening sights abroad,
Till morning in the land of Nod.

Try as I like to find the way,
I never can get back by day,
Nor can remember plain and clear
The curious music that I hear.

– Robert Louis Stevenson

THE LITTLE LAND

When at home alone I sit,
And am very tired of it,
I have just to shut my eyes
To go sailing through the skies—
To go sailing far away
To the pleasant Land of Play.

– Robert Louis Stevenson

NARCISSA

Some of the girls are playing jacks.
Some are playing ball.
But small Narcissa is not playing
Anything at all.

Small Narcissa sits upon
A brick in her back yard
And looks at tiger-lilies,
And shakes her pigtails hard.

First she is an ancient queen
In pomp and purple veil.
Soon she is a singing wind.
And, next, a nightingale.

How fine to be Narcissa,
A-changing all like that!
While sitting still, as still, as still,
As anyone ever sat!

– Gwendolyn Brooks

FOREIGN LANDS

Up into the cherry tree
Who should climb but little me?
I held the trunk with both my hands
And looked abroad on foreign lands.

I saw the next door garden lie,
Adorned with flowers, before my eye,
And many pleasant places more
That I had never seen before.

I saw the dimpling river pass
And be the sky's blue looking-glass;
The dusty roads go up and down
With people tramping in to town.

If I could find a higher tree
Farther and farther I should see,
To where the grown-up river slips
Into the sea among the ships,

To where the roads on either hand
Lead onward into fairy land,
Where all the children dine at five,
And all the playthings come alive.

– Robert Louis Stevenson

THE NORTHERN SEAS

Up! up! let us a voyage take;
    Why sit we here at ease?
Find us a vessel tight and snug,
    Bound for the northern seas.

I long to see the northern lights
    With their rushing splendors fly,
Like living things with flaming wings,
    Wide o'er the wondrous sky.

I long to see those icebergs vast,
    With heads all crowned with snow,
Whose green roots sleep in the awful deep,
    Two hundred fathoms low.

I long to hear the thundering crash
    Of their terrific fall,
And the echoes from a thousand cliffs
    Like lonely voices call.

There shall we see the fierce white bear,
    The sleepy seals aground,
And the spouting whales that to and fro
    Sail with a dreary sound.

And while the unsetting sun shines on
    Through the still heaven's deep blue,
We'll traverse the azure waves, the herds
    Of the dread sea-horse to view.

We'll pass the shores of solemn pine,
    Where wolves and black bears prowl;
And away to the rocky isles of mist,
    To rouse the northern fowl.

And there in the wastes of the silent sky,
    With the silent earth below,
We shall see far off to his lonely rock
    The lonely eagle go.

Then softly, softly will we tread
    By inland streams, to see
Where the pelican of the silent North
    Sits there all silently.

– Mary Howitt

POETRY

AT ODDS

THERE ONCE WERE TWO CATS OF KILKENNY

There once were two cats of Kilkenny,
Each thought there was one cat too many,
So they fought and they fit,
And they scratched and they bit,
Till, excepting their nails
And the tips of their tails,
Instead of two cats, there weren't any.

– Anonymous

ONE STORMY NIGHT

Two little kittens,
    One stormy night,
Began to quarrel,
    And then to fight.

One had a mouse,
    The other had none;
And that's the way
    The quarrel begun.

"I'll have that mouse,"
    Said the bigger cat.
"YOU'LL have that mouse?
    We'll see about that!"

"I WILL have that mouse,"
    Said the eldest son.
"You SHAN'T have that mouse,"
    Said the little one.

The old woman seized
    Her sweeping broom,
And swept both kittens
    Right out of the room.

The ground was covered
    With frost and snow,
And the two little kittens
    Had nowhere to go.

They lay and shivered
On a mat at the door
While the old woman
Was sweeping the floor.

And then they crept in,
As quiet as mice,
All wet with the snow,
And as cold as ice,

And found it much better,
That stormy night,
To lie by the fire
Than to quarrel and fight.

– Anonymous

THE DUEL

The gingham dog and the calico cat
Side by side on the table sat;
'Twas half-past twelve, and (what do you think!)
Nor one nor t'other had slept a wink!
    The old Dutch clock and the Chinese plate
    Appeared to know as sure as fate
There was going to be a terrible spat.
    (I wasn't there; I simply state
    What was told to me by the Chinese plate!)

The gingham dog went "Bow-wow-wow!"
And the calico cat replied "Mee-ow!"
The air was littered, an hour or so,
With bits of gingham and calico,
    While the old Dutch clock in the chimney place
    Up with its hands before its face,
For it always dreaded a family row!
    (Now mind: I'm telling you
    What the old Dutch clock declares is true!)

The Chinese plate looked very blue,
And wailed, "Oh, dear! What shall we do!"
But the gingham dog and the calico cat
Wallowed this way and tumbled that,
    Employing every tooth and claw
    In the awfullest way you ever saw—
And, oh! How the gingham and calico flew!
    (Don't fancy I exaggerate—
    I got my news from the Chinese plate!)

Next morning, where the two had sat
They found no trace of dog or cat:
And some folks think unto this day
That burglars stole that pair away!
    But the truth about the cat and pup
    Is this: they ate each other up!
Now what do you really think of that!
    (The old Dutch clock, it told me so,
    And that is how I came to know.)

– *Eugene Field*

THE SPIDER AND THE FLY

"Will you walk into my parlor?"
　　Said the Spider to the Fly;
"'Tis the prettiest little parlor
　　That ever you did spy.

"The way into my parlor
　　Is up a winding stair,
And I have many curious things
　　To show when you are there."

"Oh, no, no," said the little Fly,
　　"To ask me is in vain;
For who goes up your winding stair
　　Can ne'er come down again."

"I'm sure you must be weary, dear,
　　With soaring up so high;
Will you rest upon my little bed?"
　　Said the Spider to the Fly.

"There are pretty curtains drawn around;
    The sheets are fine and thin,
And if you like to rest awhile,
    I'll snugly tuck you in!"

"Oh, no, no," said the little Fly,
    "For I've often heard it said,
They never, never wake again,
    Who sleep upon your bed."

Said the cunning Spider to the Fly:
    "Dear friend, what can I do
To prove the warm affection
    I've always felt for you?"

"I have within my pantry
    Good store of all that's nice:
I'm sure you're very welcome—
    Will you please to take a slice?"

"Sweet creature!" said the Spider,
    "You're witty and you're wise;
How handsome are your gauzy wings:
    How brilliant are your eyes!"

"I have a little looking-glass
    Upon my parlor shelf;
If you'll step in one moment, dear,
    You shall behold yourself."

"I thank you gentle sir," she said,
    "For what you're pleased to say,
And, bidding you good-morning now,
    I'll call another day."

The Spider turned him round about,
    And went into his den,
For well he knew the silly Fly
    Would soon come back again.

So he wove a subtle web
    In a little corner sly,
And set his table ready
    To dine upon the Fly.

Then came out to his door again,
    And merrily did sing:
"Come hither, hither, pretty Fly,
    With the pearl and silver wing;

"Your robes are green and purple—
    There's a crest upon your head;
Your eyes are like the diamond bright,
    But mine are dull as lead!"

Alas, alas! How very soon
    This silly little Fly,
Hearing his wily, flattering words,
    Came slowly flittering by;

With buzzing wings she hung aloft,
    Then near and nearer drew,
Thinking only of her brilliant eyes,
    And green and purple hue—

Thinking only of her crested head—
    Poor, foolish thing! At last,
Up jumped the cunning Spider,
    And fiercely held her fast.

He dragged her up his winding stair,
  Into his dismal den,
Within his little parlor—
  But she ne'er came out again.

And now, dear little children,
  Who may this story read,
To idle, silly, flattering words,
  I pray you ne'er give heed.

Unto an evil counsellor
  Close heart and ear and eye,
And take a lesson from this tale
  Of the Spider and the Fly.

— *Mary Howitt*

POETRY

FOR THE FUN OF IT

Come live and be merry,
And join with me,
To sing the sweet chorus
Of "Ha, ha, he!"

– William Blake

From THE WALRUS
AND THE CARPENTER

"The time has come," the Walrus said,
   "To talk of many things:
Of shoes—and ships—and sealing-wax—
   Of cabbages—and kings—
And why the sea is boiling hot—
   And whether pigs have wings."

– Lewis Caroll

'TWAS MIDNIGHT

'Twas midnight on the ocean,
Not a streetcar was in sight;
The sun was shining brightly,
For it rained all day that night.
'Twas a summer day in winter
And snow was raining fast,
As a barefoot boy with shoes on
Stood sitting in the grass.

– Anonymous

GODFREY GORDON GUSTAVUS GORE

Godfrey Gordon Gustavus Gore—
No doubt you have heard the name before—
Was a boy who never would shut the door!

The wind might whistle, the wind might roar,
And teeth be aching, and throats be sore,
But still he never would shut the door.

His father would beg, his mother implore,
"Godfrey Gordon Gustavus Gore,
We really *do* wish you would shut the door!"

Their hands they wrung, their hair they tore;
But Godfrey Gordon Gustavus Gore
Was deaf as the buoy out at the Nore.

When he walked forth the folks would roar,
"Godfrey Gordon Gustavus Gore,
Why don't you think to shut the door?"

They rigged out a shutter with a sail and an oar,
And threatened to pack off Gustavus Gore
On a voyage of penance to Singapore.

But he begged for mercy, and said, "No more!
Pray do not send me to Singapore
On a shutter, and then I will shut the door!"

"You will?" said his parents; "then keep to shore!
But mind you do! For the plague is sore
Of a fellow that never will shut the door,
Godfrey Gordon Gustavus Gore!"

– William B. Rands

THE ELEPHANT

When people call this beast to mind,
 They marvel more and more
At such a *little* tail behind,
 So LARGE a trunk before.

– Hilaire Belloc

THE GRASSHOPPER
AND THE ELEPHANT

Way down south where bananas grow,
A grasshopper stepped on an elephant's toe.
The elephant said, with tears in his eyes,
"Pick on somebody your own size."

– Anonymous

ELETELEPHONY

Once there was an elephant,
Who tried to use the telephant—
No! no! I mean an elephone
Who tried to use the telephone—
(Dear me! I am not certain quite
That even now I've got it right.)

Howe'er it was, he got his trunk
Entangled in the telephunk;
The more he tried to get it free,
The louder buzzed the telephee—
(I fear I'd better drop the song
Of elephop and telephong!)

– Laura E. Richards

Text Credits and Sources

Poems:

"Eletelephony" by Laura E. Richards. Reprinted with the kind permission of Mrs. Laura E. Putnam, granddaughter of the poet.

"Narcissa" from *Bronzeville Boys and Girls* ©1956 by Gwendolyn Brooks Blakey. Reprinted by permission of HarperCollins Publishers.

Stories adapted from:

Child Life in Tale and Fable, A Third Reader, Etta Austin Blaisdell and Mary Frances Blaisdell (New York: Macmillan, 1908)

Everyday Classics, Third Reader, Franklin T. Baker, Ashley H. Thorndike, and Mildred Batchelder (New York: Macmillan, 1922)

Fifty Famous Stories Retold, James Baldwin (New York: American Book Company, 1896)

The Merrill Readers, Third Reader, Franklin B. Dyer and Mary J. Brady (New York: Charles E. Merrill Company, 1915)

The Natural Method Readers, A Second Reader, Hannah T. McManus and John H. Haaren (New York: Charles Scribner's Sons, 1915)

The Progressive Road to Reading, Book Three, Georgine Burchill, William L. Ettinger, and Edgar Dubs Shimar (New York: Silver, Burdett and Company, 1920)

Story Hour Readers Revised, Book Three, Ida Coe and Alice C. Dillion, (New York: American Book Company, 1914)

Swinton's Third Reader (New York: American Book Company, 1882)

Editor: John Holdren

Art Director: Steve Godwin

Designer: Jayoung Cho

Illustrators:
Dan Boris
Jayoung Cho
Vince McGinley
Deborah Wolfe Ltd: (Jeff LeVan)

ISBN: 1-931728-35-6